mac 2006

Cartoons from the *Daily Mail*

Stan McMurtry **mac**
Edited by Mark Bryant

ROBSON BOOKS

To Joan and John and Janet and Brian

First published in the United Kingdom in 2006 by
Robson Books
151 Freston Road
London
W10 6TH

An imprint of Anova Books Company Ltd

ISBN 1 86105 985 X

A CIP catalogue record for this book is available from the British Library.

10 9 8 7 6 5 4 3 2 1

Reproduction by SX Composing DTP, Rayleigh, Essex
Printed and bound by MPG Books Ltd, Bodmin, Cornwall

This book can be ordered direct from the publisher.
Contact the marketing department, but try your bookshop first.

www.anovabooks.com

Bow Street Magistrates' Court heard how a young hacker from North London, working from his bedroom, gained access to nearly 100 US Government computers, including those at the Pentagon and NASA as well as the US Army and Navy.

'I'm warning you, Nigel. If you try sending the American fleet to nuke Russia again you'll go to bed without any tea.'

29 July 2005

There was a dramatic fall in the sale of thongs, especially amongst the smart set, with Harvey Nichols recording a 43% drop in the market for this kind of women's underwear.

'I'm not sure but I think I'm still wearing an unfashionable thong – and I'd like it removed.'   *2 August*

Two British-born Islamic preachers interviewed on BBC 2 TV's *Newsnight* programme appeared to praise the 7 July London suicide bombers.

3 August

In a six-hour spacewalk 220 miles above earth, US astronaut Steve Robinson performed repairs to the space-shuttle *Discovery*. Meanwhile, as civil war threatened, there were increasing calls for the USA to withdraw its troops from Iraq.

'Houston. We have a problem.' *4 August*

At the unveiling of a new £100,000 waxwork statue of Prince William, a spokesman for Madame Tussauds in London reported that it had been made of especially hard material to withstand kissing from female admirers.

'If you must hug and kiss the exhibits, miss, could you make it just a quick peck?'   *5 August*

Royal officials at Clarence House denied rumours that Prince Charles had had a hairweave or transplant when he visited a whisky distillery in Scotland with apparently thicker hair than he had had at a polo match two weeks earlier.

'Well, they got that wrong, Camilla darling. They say the new hair came from the back of my head.'   *9 August*

A 45-year-old mother-of-five from Yorkshire abandoned her schoolgirl daughter in Britain to live in Turkey with a 26-year-old Turkish man she had met on holiday.

'Surprise! I've left my daughter at home to be with you, Mustapha. She's only 53 but dammit you only live once!' *10 August*

There was a public outcry when Syrian-born extremist Muslim cleric Omar Bakri Mohammed, who had lived on benefits in the UK for 19 years and was on holiday in Lebanon, said he planned to return to Britain for a £7,500 heart operation on the NHS.

'Y'know, if Bakri Mohammed does turn up here, I think we've got just the man for the job.' *11 August*

After 500 catering staff were sacked for going on unofficial strike, long-haul passengers on British Airways flights from Heathrow were given vouchers to buy food and drink to take on their journeys.

'Could you try to keep the plane steady? Our barbecue keeps falling over.' *12 August*

In her autobiography, *Learning to Fly*, former Spice Girl Victoria Beckham admitted that she had never read a book. Meanwhile, as the A-level pass rate rose for the 23rd year running, reaching 97%, many felt that this former 'gold standard' of education was now worthless.

'Neither have I and I've just got six A-levels.'   *16 August*

A study by academics at Plymouth University working for the International Fund for Animal Welfare revealed a worrying new boom in the sale of endangered species on the internet, including gorillas, giraffes, turtles, monkeys and rare Amazonian parrots.

'My husband also bought three monkeys and a parrot but they've all mysteriously disappeared.' *17 August*

A couple were arrested while attempting to have sex in the toilet of an aeroplane on a return holiday flight from Tenerife. The 'Mile High Club' pair, previously strangers, had met when the flight was delayed by eight and a half hours.

'It's very inconvenient. People keep wanting to use the toilet cubicle as a loo!'   *18 August*

'Go easy on him, boss. Just as he was getting over not fox-hunting, Prince Charles decides to give up playing polo, too.'

19 August

Aged 62, wrinkly rocker Sir Mick Jagger and the Rolling Stones kicked off their latest world tour – estimated to earn them £10 million each – with a sell-out concert at Boston's Fenway Park baseball stadium.

'I think I've pulled. Mick's asked me back to his place for cocoa and a digestive biscuit.'   *24 August*

Criticised in the past for using his position to arrange free holidays for himself and his family, Prime Minister Tony Blair was photographed on a beach in Barbados playing the ukulele to a group of friends.

'Keep going, Tony. We've nearly got enough for some free ice creams.' *25 August*

There were fears for an increase in 'binge drinking' when it was revealed that Government proposals for a new Licensing Act would not only extend pub and bar opening times but would also allow supermarkets to sell alcohol 24 hours a day.

'Shorry I'm late. I've jusht been down to the shoopermarket for shome eggsh.' *26 August*

For the first time in many years, Australia's cricket team found themselves trailing badly to
England in the annual Test Match, with only one match left to play to win the Ashes.

'Come on now, Bruce. Show you're a good loser. Take our Pom neighbour a beer and apologise for shearing
him and nailing him to the shed.' *30 August*

EU Trade Commissioner Peter Mandelson tried to mediate with European manufacturers in the so-called 'bra wars' dispute as millions of items of cheap clothing from China – including bras, pullovers and trousers – were impounded in European ports.

'Honestly, Ingrid. Until Mandelson gets your size 48 supercup bras into the country,
I think those blue ones are very sexy.' *31 August*

An article in *Nature* reported that an international group of scientists had succeeded in working out the DNA of a chimpanzee and discovered that 96% of human and chimp genes are identical.

'Aren't you glad we only share 96% of our genes with humans?'   *2 September*

Motorists braced themselves for further rises in the cost of fuel as Shell and BP unveiled plans to upgrade their petrol stations because their pumps were unable to display prices higher than 99.99 pence per litre.

'That's my final offer. I'll give you five gallons for the shoes and the watch.'   *6 September*

Researchers at the University of Oxford announced that they had developed an 'intelligent car' incorporating 'blink sensors' that detected when drivers were drowsy and triggered invigorating scent sprays and other devices to wake them up.

'Don't keep blinking. The car thinks you're nodding off.' *7 September*

As the final Test Match against Australia opened at the Oval in London, England's captain Michael Vaughan backed a campaign to urge supporters across the country to sing William Blake's famous hymn *Jerusalem* at 10.25am that morning.

'Oh no! I must've died. I can hear angels singing *Jerusalem*.'   *8 September*

While hopes ran high for England's cricketers, panic-buying began at petrol stations after threats of blockades at oil refineries by hauliers whose businesses faced ruin because of the rocketing price of fuel in the wake of Hurricane Katrina.

'I was only going to get a gallon or two until I noticed the driver was watching the cricket.'   *13 September*

There was widespread jubilation amongst cricket fans as England beat Australia and won the
Ashes for the first time in 18 years.

'I've washed that ugly old egg-cup thing. It was full of ashes.' *14 September*

In a landmark case, the European Court of Human Rights in Strasbourg overturned a 450-year old British law and granted a 37-year-old British woman the right to marry her 58-year-old father-in-law.

'For the last time, mother – Bill and I are very happy!' *15 September*

A survey by the media consultancy Screen Digest revealed that though Britain now has 24 children's TV channels, it also broadcasts 27 X-rated adult channels via satellite or digital pay-per-view, making it the leading country for TV pornography in Europe.

'Oh no! Not another Teletubbies gangbang!' *16 September*

At the Labour Party's annual Conference in Brighton many thought that Chancellor Gordon Brown's impressive speech bore all the hallmarks of a future Prime Minister and led to speculation as to when he would take over the leadership of the Party.

'Who's the man with the big ears standing next to the Prime Minister?'   *27 September*

The following day Tony Blair dispelled all doubt about his position by repeating that he intended to serve out his full term of office, adding that, though the Government had made mistakes in the past, he would be at the head of the 'change-makers'.

'I just hope that bit about us being "change-makers" has inspired a few people.' *28 September*

At the Labour Party Conference Education Secretary Ruth Kelly declared a war on junk food in schools, banning them from canteens and vending machines. Meanwhile, Japanese scientists in Tokyo discovered and filmed a 26-foot-long giant squid.

'Spit that out, Wayne! You heard what Ruth Kelly said. You're not supposed to eat junk food.' *29 September*

A joint study by NASA and the University of Colorado claimed that the Arctic ice-cap could disappear within 100 years because of global warming. The World Wildlife Fund added that, as a result, polar bears could be extinct by the end of this century.

'You mark my words. If the Arctic ice-cap does melt, in no time at all we'll be inundated by penguins eating our fish.'

30 September

At the Conservative Party Conference in Blackpool, reference was made to an 82-year-old man who had been forcibly evicted from Labour's conference for crying 'nonsense' during Jack Straw's speech justifying the continued presence of British troops in Iraq.

'. . . and rest assured, our security team will not be giving hecklers here the same appalling treatment as that dished out at Labour's conference.'   *4 October*

Award-winning comedian and writer Ronnie Barker, best known for his long partnership with Ronnie Corbett in TV's *The Two Ronnies* and for his roles as the convict Fletcher in *Porridge* and the shopkeeper Arkwright in *Open All Hours*, died aged 76.

'. . . and it's goodnight from him.' *5 October*

As Tory leadership hopefuls David Davis, Kenneth Clarke, Liam Fox and David Cameron made speeches to the Conservative Party Conference, the *Daily Mail* serialised the memoirs of Sharon Osbourne, star of TV's pop-talent show *The X Factor*.

'Psst. Ask Sharon Osbourne who's winning so far.' *6 October*

A Dorset estate agent put on sale a small run-down 40-year-old shed near Portland Bill lighthouse – with no electricity, water or sewage – for £20,000, describing it as 'beach hut' though it was two miles from the nearest beach.

'Women! Can you understand them? She didn't even let me carry her over the threshold.' *7 October*

Trade Secretary Alan Johnson announced plans to extend paternity leave to six months.

'Cooee, darling. I'm almost at the end of my paternity leave again.' *11 October*

Official Department of Education figures revealed that only 56% of British children leaving primary school passed all of the traditional 'three Rs'. Nearly half of the country's eleven-year-olds were unable to master reading, writing and arithmetic.

'What kind of crappy school are you running here? My lad's 11 and he can't even read!' *12 October*

Despite being criticised for poor-quality programming and frequent repeats, the BBC announced that it planned to raise the cost of the colour TV licence to £200 to help fund the switch from analogue to digital broadcasting.

'Please, George. If we all promise to chip in for the new TV licence, can we have the telly back?' *13 October*

As the killer bird-flu virus reached Romania from Turkey, Britain's Chief Medical Officer, Sir Liam Donaldson, warned that if it was able to cross over into humans there could be a pandemic, with as many as 50,000 victims in the UK alone.

'This is a raid, buster! Hand over the parrot food or I sneeze!' *18 October*

An official Prison Service instruction broadened the scope of religions that inmates could practise to include paganism, druidism, voodoo, shamanism, witchcraft and the worship of Norse gods such as Odin and Thor.

'I must ask you to leave, sir. Visiting hours are 2pm to 4pm, Wednesdays and Sundays only.'   *19 October*

The latest official police figures revealed that violent crime was up by 6% in England and Wales. Much of the increase was blamed on binge drinking.

'Before we go in, I'd like to apologise profusely for beating you to a pulp when we come out.' *21 October*

A parrot imported from South America, which died while in an Essex quarantine centre, was found to have contracted the killer bird-flu virus.

'He sits watching TV all day, moaning and groaning and having me running around getting him things – I think he's got human flu.' *25 October*

In an attempt to cut Britain's soaring unwanted pregnancy rate, it was announced that a new kind of contraceptive injection – which was cheaper than the Pill and could last up to three months – would be offered on the NHS to all women over 16.

'This is the new NHS contraceptive revolution which is long-lasting and cheaper than the Pill.' *26 October*

Health Secretary Patricia Hewitt unveiled plans to ban smoking in all restaurants and pubs that served food. Smoking would only be allowed in pubs in separate rooms that did not serve drinks and were situated well away from the bar area.

'Hurry up, you lot. There are other people dying for a fag too, y'know.'   *27 October*

In a BBC interview Prince Charles – who had installed many eco-friendly devices at his home at Highgrove House in Gloucestershire – said that climate change was 'the greatest challenge to face mankind'.

'**He's probably just given another speech on excessive fuel consumption and the environment.**' *28 October*

As the debate over the wisdom of allowing 24-hour drinking continued, the Government introduced a 'Britishness' test for immigrants who wished to apply for a British passport.

'Congratulations, Mr. Sajeed. You've passed the Government's Britishness test.'   *1 November*

Work and Pensions Secretary David Blunkett, who had been forced to resign as Home Secretary in 2004 over scandals in his private life, hit the headlines again when it was revealed that he had shares in a company that was bidding for a Government contract.

'So, you think he's no longer responsible for his actions and you want power of attorney?' *2 November*

Rebekah Wade, 37-year-old editor of the *Sun*, spent eight hours in custody for allegedly attacking her husband, *EastEnders* hard man Ross Kemp.

'I let her off with a caution as long as I can be on Page 3 tomorrow.'   *4 November*

Deputy Prime Minister John Prescott announced that the Valuation Office would be revaluing all properties in Britain and that those whose homes overlooked the sea, countryside, parks or golf courses could expect to pay higher council tax bills next year.

'I don't know why you're getting so upset. It won't affect us.'   *8 November*

The Prime Minister was at the centre of a 'cash for honours' scandal when leaked documents revealed that 18 millionaires who had donated a total of £16 million to Labour Party funds over the past nine years had been given peerages.

'Sorry, lads. I can't buy a round. I've just sent my last twenty quid to Tony Blair.' *9 November*

In a major challenge to Tony Blair's authority, the Terrorism Bill – allowing police to hold terror suspects for 90 days without charge – was defeated in the House of Commons despite Chancellor Gordon Brown being flown back from Tel Aviv to vote.

'This is your captain speaking. Fasten your seatbelt please, we are approaching Tel Aviv airport yet again . . .'
10 November

The future for the Prime Minister – whose 'freebie' holidays had included staying in Barbados as the guest of pop star Sir Cliff Richard – looked increasingly precarious, with many expecting Gordon Brown to take over his job in the near future.

'I fear the worst – Gordon's booked his first freebie holiday at Cliff Richard's villa in Barbados.' *11 November*

In an attempt to thwart potential suicide bombers, Transport Secretary Alistair Darling announced plans to carry out trials of new body scanners and luggage X-ray machines on selected underground and airport rail services in London early next year.

'Just the luggage, Benskin. The train's already three hours late.' *15 November*

The new Licensing Act – which would enable 700 pubs, clubs and supermarkets to be granted licences to serve alcohol up to 24 hours a day – was passed in the House of Commons by 302 votes to 228.

'We losht the vote on binge drinking.'   *16 November*

In an effort to combat the pension-funds crisis the Government backed plans to extend the age of official retirement to 67, forcing millions to work two extra years before being entitled to receive a state pension.

'Isn't that nice, dear? As you didn't make it to your pension, the company have had a whip-round and got you a watch.'

18 November

Mac took a break to travel the world from December 2005 to February 2006 but continued to send back 'postcards' to the *Daily Mail* from various locations. This one is from Fiji.

'I wonder what they do if somebody burns their feet?' *15 December*

Mac's 'postcard' from New Zealand.

'Oh go on, give them a game or we'll have the Haka all night.' *29 December*

A drawing sent while Mac was visiting Kakadu National Park in Australia.

'Dear All. Can't help feeling smug after learning how cold it is in Britain. Everything here is so perfect.' *11 January 2006*

The fourth of Mac's cartoons from overseas, this one also features his wife Liz.

'I wonder what time they open in the morning?' *17 January*

'. . . then straight after trouncing you lot in the Rugby World Cup we stuffed you for the Ashes and . . .
hey, great! Are we going to have a real Aussie barbie?'   *7 February*

After leaving Australia Mac arrived in Hong Kong just after the publication of a Danish cartoon depicting Mohammed as a terrorist which caused outrage in the Muslim world.

'. . . Name – Mac . . . Duration of Stay – 3 days . . . Occupation – Cartoonist.'   *13 February*

A survey revealed that almost 2,000 of the Metropolitan Police's 30,000 officers had registered outside jobs or business interests, including floristry, plumbing, modelling and working as masseurs.

'That's the choice, ducky. Either accompany me to the station or have a nice massage and pedicure for just £25.'

21 February

In the court case between Prince Charles and the *Mail on Sunday* over publication of extracts from his private journals, it was revealed that the prince had 'bombarded' Government ministers with letters about policy and saw himself as a political dissident.

'**More junk mail – pizza adverts, double-glazing brochures, letters from Prince Charles . . .**' *23 February*

An armed gang stole more than £50 million from a Securitas depot in Tonbridge, Kent, in Britain's biggest-ever cash robbery. Meanwhile, angry customers faced a 22% rise in their energy bills as Centrica – owners of British Gas – announced record profits.

'Turn up the central heating? Have you seen this gas bill?'   *24 February*

After the sale of P&O to Dubai, British businesses suddenly seemed to be swamped by takeover bids from foreign companies, amongst them the Lancashire glassmaking firm of Pilkington which was bought by Nippon Sheet Glass of Japan.

'Dammit, Carruthers! Who will the Japanese get their hands on next?'   *1 March*

As the killer bird-flu virus spread slowly across Europe there were new fears that it could cross species when a domestic cat died after eating an infected bird on an island off the north coast of Germany.

'That's very naughty. If you must kill cats, don't keep bringing them into the house.' *2 March*

When her City lawyer husband David Mills was arrested to face charges of bribery and corruption brought by Italian police, beleaguered Culture Secretary Tessa Jowell denied all knowledge of his devious financial affairs.

'From now on, David, we'll have to be more open with each other . . . now, is there anything else you haven't told me?'

3 March

A BBC 2 TV documentary, *The Family That Walks On All Fours*, filmed the lives of a Kurdish family of five from south-eastern Turkey who were unable to walk upright and had to resort to 'bear crawling'.

'Walkies!'   *8 March*

Following a rise in allegations of rape by women who had been binge drinking, the Government launched a £500,000 advertising campaign to warn men that they must obtain consent from their partners before having sex.

'Speak up, luv. I, Sharlene of Finsbury Park, do solemnly consent to allow the amorous advances of Kevin Stanley Swindley, now residing in Woking . . .'   *9 March*

Wildlife protection campaigners welcomed the decision by Environment Minister Ben Bradshaw to introduce an Animal Welfare Bill which would outlaw the use of wild animals such as elephants, bears and monkeys in travelling circuses.

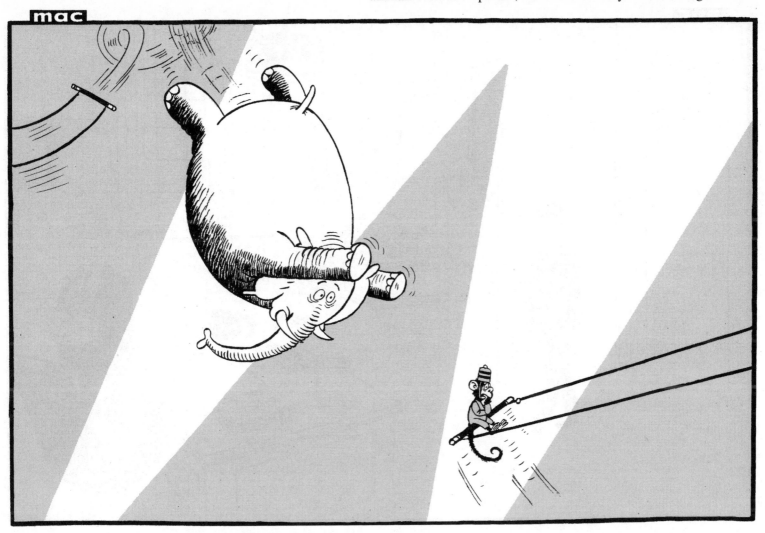

'Humans! Can anyone understand them? They spend years teaching us new tricks then they ban performing animals!'
10 March

Home Secretary Charles Clarke launched an official inquiry following allegations that Britain's top policeman, Metropolitan Police Commissioner Sir Ian Blair, had secretly tape recorded a phone conversation he had had with Attorney General Lord Goldsmith.

'Ah, Home Secretary . . . testing, testing . . . one, two, three, four . . . Monday, Tuesday, Wednesday. I believe you wanted to see me . . .' *14 March*

In an effort to crack down on 'pew-jumper' parents who pretended to be Christians in order to get their children into high-achieving Anglican schools, Church of England officials introduced new entry regulations, including proof of baptism.

'**I can't go through with this, Fiona – he'll have to go to the comprehensive.**' *15 March*

Less than a month after the Securitas robbery in Kent, £15 million of the stolen cash was found dumped in a van parked near the Channel Tunnel. Meanwhile, the 'cash for honours' scandal continued to hit the headlines as more details emerged.

' "Sorry, lads," says Fingers, "we're going to 'ave to dump some of the fifty-three million quid we nicked from Securitas." So I rings up Tony . . .' *17 March*

Under increasing pressure over the 'cash for honours' row, Tony Blair released the names of 12 millionaires who had made secret loans to the Labour Party. Furious at this breach of confidentiality, many of them threatened to ask for their money back.

'Are there any other debts you haven't mentioned, Tony? The bailiffs have been in.'   *22 March*

In Chancellor Gordon Brown's Budget road tax was raised to £215 a year for four-wheel-drive, gas-guzzling 'Chelsea Tractors' and people carriers but cut altogether for the greenest vehicles, such as electric cars.

'Aw, c'mon, hop in. Think of all the road tax we'll be saving.' *24 March*

Damning reports by the Government's Healthcare Commission, Audit Commission and Commission for Social Care Inspection accused staff in Britain's hospitals and day-care centres of 'patronising and thoughtless treatment' of elderly patients.

'Say nothing. We're digging a tunnel in the TV room.'   *28 March*

As Prince Charles and Camilla Parker Bowles began the last leg of their journey through India, a new biography of the American singer and actress Barbra Streisand alleged that she had once had a romantic relationship with the prince.

'Instead of another of your boring old speeches, Highness, can we persuade your lovely wife Barbra to give us a song?'

29 March

In a scathing report, former NatWest boss Sir Derek Wanless called for an end to means testing of the elderly, which forced 70,000 people a year to sell their houses to pay for places in care homes.

'I thought your mother was selling her house to go into a care home.'   *31 March*

Two years after hitting the headlines for his involvement in a high-profile love-affair, Conservative Party Higher Education spokesman and former *Spectator* editor, Boris Johnson, father of four, was accused of having a second extramarital relationship.

'You're strangely quiet tonight, Boris darling – have you told your wife yet?' *4 April*

As it was revealed that billions of gallons of water are wasted through leaks each year, hosepipe bans were introduced in the south-east of England and members of the public were encouraged to report on neighbours who defied the ruling.

'You heard me, buster! Drop the hose and come out with your hands up!'   *5 April*

To ease the pressure on Britain's overcrowded prisons the Home Office instructed police to issue cautions to serial offenders rather than take them to court. Meanwhile, Scotland Yard planned to introduce gay quotas in the Metropolitan Police.

'I thought you were only supposed to give me a caution.' *6 April*

While continuing his officer training course at the Royal Military Academy at Sandhurst in Berkshire, Prince Harry visited a local lap-dancing club with a group of friends.

'Just serve the tea, Jenkins. Prince Harry has to get back to camp.' *11 April*

Romani Prodi, Italy's new Prime Minister, celebrated with his wife Flavia after narrowly beating Silvio Berlusconi, who had been Tony Blair's staunchest ally in Europe and whose hospitality he and Cherie had enjoyed on many occasions.

'Berlusconi has to admit it, Flavia darling. His fans have deserted him . . . hello, who's this?' *12 April*

Women's rights groups reacted with horror when the Lord Chief Justice's Sentencing Guidelines Council declared that men convicted of beating up their wives or partners could escape jail sentences if they showed 'genuine remorse' for their actions.

'Remember, sir. Your freedom depends on this answer – do you feel genuine remorse about trying to beat up your wife?'

13 April

After 18 years as presenter of BBC Radio 4's weekly *Desert Island Discs*, 60-year-old veteran broadcaster Sue Lawley announced that she would be leaving the programme to pursue new broadcasting and business interests.

'Good grief, you're right. It *is* Sue Lawley!'   *14 April*

As the 'cash for honours' scandal gathered pace, the Cabinet Office revealed that Cherie Blair had spent £127,000 of taxpayers' money refurbishing No.10 Downing Street between 1999 and 2005.

'This bit was the most expensive. It's an escape tunnel in case the police come looking for Daddy about peerages.'

18 April

In its annual survey the Association of Independent Special Medical Accountants revealed that the average wage of GPs had risen by 25% over the past two years with some now earning as much as £250,000 a year.

'The doctor's butler will see you now.'   *19 April*

The price of crude oil soared to its highest level since 1983, with pump prices reaching £5 a gallon in Britain. Meanwhile, it was reported that the highest-paid presenter on BBC Radio 2 earned £530,000 for working three hours a week (£60 a minute).

'Wow! A whole tankful – he must be either a doctor or a Radio 2 DJ!'   *20 April*

The Queen celebrated her 80th birthday. She received more than 20,000 birthday cards.

'If that's the post, Philip dear, will you see if there are any cards for me?' *21 April*

Health Secretary Patricia Hewitt faced a furious backlash after claiming that 'despite the headlines the NHS has just had its best year yet'. Meanwhile, a report by the Royal College of Nursing said there had been 13,000 redundancies since October.

'That's a relief. It's all just an exaggeration by the newspapers, according to Patricia Hewitt.' *25 April*

Britain's biggest and most profitable retailer Tesco, with nearly 2,000 outlets and profits of £2.25 billion, announced massive expansion plans including the opening of 125 new or improved stores over the next 12 months.

'Turn left at this Tesco, straight on till you reach another Tesco, over the bridge to a small Tesco and the post office is opposite where they're building a new Tesco.' *26 April*

The overweight Deputy PM John Prescott hit the headlines when he admitted he had used his official residences – funded by the taxpayer – to carry on an affair with his diary secretary. Later two other women also claimed to have had relationships with him.

'Those poor women. Imagine what it must be like sleeping with John Prescott.' *2 May*

Addressing a conference in Harrogate, the General Secretary of the Association of Head Teachers claimed that middle-class children were under-performing at school because their parents were too soft and allowed them to do what they liked.

'. . . and you can stay in your bedroom with no tea or television till you've finished my homework!'   *3 May*

After the freed foreign convicts scandal Home Secretary Charles Clarke's job was again on the line when it was discovered that a man wanted for the murder of a policewoman should have been deported to his native Somalia seven months earlier.

'Looks like the British have started deporting their undesirables at long last.' *4 May*

It was announced that a Sussex woman, who would be 63 in September, was seven months pregnant after receiving fertility treatment in Italy.

'Damn! Have you ever walked into a room then forgotten what you came in for?' *5 May*

There was a police inquiry after ten members of the Tottenham Hotspur football team were struck down by a mystery food bug just hours before they lost a crucial match which knocked them out of a place in the Champions League.

'Hurry up, lads. You're 53-0 down.' *9 May*

As the Government admitted it had no idea how many illegal immigrants were living in Britain, Communities Secretary Ruth Kelly determined to push through Labour's massive new house-building programme in southern England despite widespread opposition.

'Actually we haven't reached Britain yet, Miss Kelly. But we'd like granite worktops and white tiles in the kitchen . . .'

11 May

Watched by Prince Charles and Camilla Parker Bowles, Prince Harry made his first appearance at the annual Combined Cavalry Old Comrades' Association parade in London's Hyde Park, wearing the traditional outfit of a suit and bowler hat.

'They all look the same to me. Which one's Prince Harry?'   *16 May*

To try and combat water shortages, a local authority in southern England imposed an official drought order, the first in Britain for ten years. Though this included a hosepipe ban and other measures, it did allow the public to have baths and showers.

'Ah, Donald. This gentleman can no longer have his monthly hosedown, so he's exercising his human rights.' *17 May*

As Sir Paul McCartney and his wife admitted that their four-year marriage was over, legal experts speculated that Lady McCartney could claim as much as £200 million of the ex-Beatle's fortune – almost £1 million for each week they had been married.

'Sorry, Trevor. I've just heard that Paul McCartney is free.' *18 May*

The Government agreed a rescue package of nearly £3 billion for Royal Mail at a time when the company announced pre-tax profits of £312 million, with 193,000 staff sharing a £100 million jackpot.

'The postman's got a hangover this morning so he's sent his butler.'   *19 May*

'Sure, that's OK. Go ahead and give somebody else the room . . . yes, we'll miss you too. Thanks for calling, Governor.'

23 May

Soon after taking over as Home Secretary, John Reid attacked his own department, saying it was 'not fit for the purpose'. Meanwhile, Tory leader David Cameron spoke at a conference about the limitations of work, emphasising the importance of 'quality of life'.

'Cameron's not saying anything new – we've known that for years.'   *24 May*

After being filmed by an outraged male neighbour, a 55-year-old district nurse from Cardigan, Wales, was charged with indecent exposure for walking in her garden in the nude.

'Avert the children's eyes! Our next-door neighbour is sunbathing in the nude again.'   *26 May*

It was revealed that a 58-year-old Suffolk farmer who grew elephant grass for thatching and animal bedding also ran a business building traditional wooden platform gallows.

'I'm not one to turn down business, George. But I reckon you should try a marriage-guidance counsellor first.'   *31 May*

The two most prominent judges in Britain – former Lord Chief Justice Lord Woolf and his successor Lord Phillips – launched an unprecedented attack on the Government and its policy on crime and sentencing.

1 June

Deputy Prime Minister John Prescott lost his grace-and-favour mansion, Dorneywood in Buckinghamshire (but kept his flat in London), after being photographed playing croquet there when he was supposed to be running the country in Tony Blair's absence.

'Looks like he's missing Dorneywood already.'   *2 June*

In a deal worth £10 billion, the Spanish construction firm Ferrovial bought British Airports Authority (BAA), owner of seven UK airports including Heathrow and Gatwick.

'You must admit he's much more fun than the man with the ping-pong bats.' *7 June*

As English football fans massed in Frankfurt, Germany, for England's first World Cup match against Paraguay, there was much speculation over the fitness of 20-year-old striker Wayne Rooney who had sustained a fractured metatarsal in his right foot.

'Oh, Lord, before we get drunk as skunks and wreck the place, a few words askin' for good news about Rooney's metatarsole wotsit where it meets the proximal phalanx . . .'   *8 June*

As National Audit Office figures revealed that the NHS was £1.3 billion in the red, it was claimed that over the past year £1 billion had been paid to management consultants and more than £1 million had been spent on hospital directors' salaries alone.

'So where are we going wrong? Have any of you managers any idea why our hospital is so much in the red?'   *9 June*

The Government announced that the proposed law banning smoking in public places was to be extended to areas where there is an 'inevitable close grouping of people' such as bus shelters, sports grounds, train platforms and the entrances to office buildings.

'Sorry, love. You've wasted your time. I only popped out here for a fag . . .' *22 June*

It was revealed that Britain's biggest water company, Thames Water, lost nearly 200 million gallons a day through leaks. Meanwhile, the Government gave the green light to a £25 billion new generation of US-made, submarine-launched Trident nuclear missiles.

'Remember saying: "Trident, what a waste of money. When would the Government ever use it?"' *23 June*

Conservative Party Leader David Cameron suggested that the Human Rights Act should be replaced by a British Bill of Rights. Meanwhile, England beat Ecuador to win a place in the World Cup quarter finals and the annual Wimbledon tennis tournament began.

'Looks like the human-rights debate over the choice of tennis or football on TV has been settled.' *27 June*

The Institution of Civil Engineers proposed the establishment of a national grid for water – similar to those for gas and electricity – with pipelines diverting water from the River Trent, Wales and the North to prevent shortages in London and the South.

'Stanley hates Southerners.'   *28 June*

As the Queen appealed for an increase of £1 million to her annual £15 million royal palaces' maintenance grant, a Royal Public Finances report revealed that the overall cost of the monarchy was now £37.4 million a year.

'People moan, Philip dear. But I can't think where we can cut back any further on expenditure.'   *29 June*

A new miracle weight-loss pill became available on prescription in the UK. Manufactured by a French pharmaceutical company, it claimed to cut 10% of body weight a year by reducing the desire to eat.

'You'll have to excuse Dorothy – she's just taken her miracle weight-loss pill.' *30 June*

Britain's sports hopes were dashed as Andy Murray lost at Wimbledon to Marcos Baghdatis of Cyprus and England were knocked out of the World Cup by Portugal (during the match Wayne Rooney was sent off for kicking a Portuguese player in the groin).

'Aw, Wayne. I was enjoying the tennis. Why did you have to kick Baghdatis in the groin?'   *4 July*

There was a public outcry when water watchdog Ofwat decided not to use its powers to fine Thames Water for its failure to stop its huge pipeline leaks at a time when the company's profits had soared to £346 million a year.

'Great news, folks. We're not being fined for all the leaks so let's keep this one till after the heatwave.'   *5 July*

US President George Bush, who had invaded Iraq without finding any weapons of mass destruction, did nothing when Communist North Korea – which is known to have nuclear weapons – launched a ballistic missile capable of striking at North America.

'Dang! Ah keep thinking ah'm gonna find a weapon of mass destruction.'   *6 July*

There were more accusations of sleaze when it was discovered that Deputy Prime Minister John Prescott had accepted hospitality at the Colorado ranch of an American billionaire who was bidding to run a supercasino in London's Millennium Dome.

'For the last time, I'm not resigning! I have a very busy job and I intend to get on with it!'   *7 July*

In a move that surprised and angered many, Conservative Party Leader David Cameron called on the public to show more love and understanding to the 'hoodie' teenage yobs responsible for the epidemic of antisocial behaviour on Britain's streets.

'What are the police doing about it? Streets full of Tory women trying to give us love and compassion. We're frightened to go out at night.'   *11 July*

Labour's long-awaited energy review gave the go-ahead to a new generation of nuclear power stations but also said that 20% of the nation's needs should come from renewable sources such as wind, wave and solar power.

'Great news, Denzil. Mr. Blair's thinkin' of buildin' some o' them great big ones up on the hill.' *12 July*

As teenage crime continued to rise, Schools Minister Lord Adonis wrote to every head teacher in England inviting them to send their most gifted pupils to be registered at the National Academy for Gifted and Talented Youth based at Warwick University.

'Well done, Wayne. The two tens, the twenty and the coins do add up to £40.23 – I have some exciting news for you . . .'

13 July

The public stripped off as Britain baked in a heatwave with temperatures the highest on record for July. Meanwhile, at Wimbledon, a male streaker interrupted the women's quarter-final match between former champion Maria Sharapova and Elena Dementieva.

'Ooh look. A streaker.'   *18 July*

Research by scientists working for the Restoration of Appearance & Function Trust held that sunscreens should not be rubbed into the skin and only work effectively if they are applied as a thick 'buttery' layer.

'Damn! I forgot about your mother. Nip out and tell her the sun went in hours ago.' *19 July*

A study by biologists at University College, London, claimed that, because of their Anglo-Saxon ancestry, most white males in Britain are genetically German and have the same Y-chromosomes as people from Friesland, Holstein and Jutland.

'I think the heat has got to him, doctor. He's just gone out to invade Poland.' *20 July*

Following allegations in a BBC documentary that a police officer involved in the investigation into the murder of Stephen Lawrence in London in 1993 had been bribed by the father of one of the suspects, Scotland Yard faced a new inquiry into the case.

'The Long Arm of the Law.'   *25 July*